MICHAEL ROSE

A Miscellany for Oboe

BOOK II

THE ASSOCIATED BOARD OF
THE ROYAL SCHOOLS OF MUSIC

for Rebecca

A MISCELLANY FOR OBOE
BOOK II

MICHAEL ROSE

Serenade

AB 2128

Caribbean Cameo

Jig

8

Aria

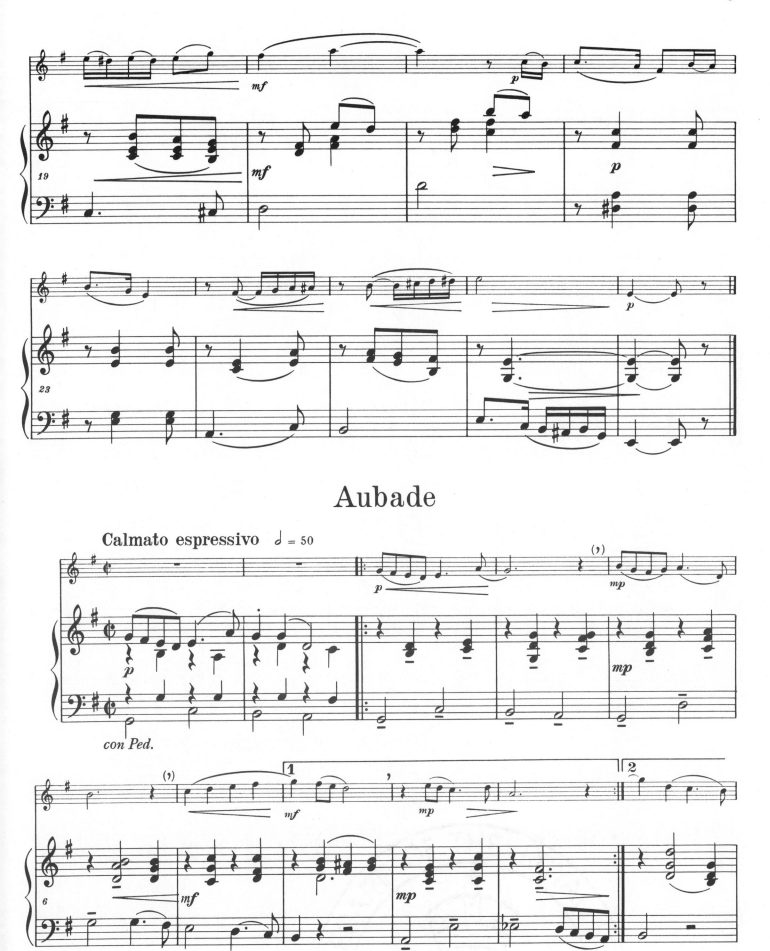

Aubade

Punch and Judy

alla Coda

molto tenuto

Molto meno mosso

Dal Segno al ✛ poi alla Coda

CODA

Romanza

Molto moderato, espressivo sempre ♩ = 80

Printed in England by Caligraving Limited Thetford Norfolk

3:08

AB 2128